Creative Colouring

Animal Wonders

Parragon

Bath • New York • Cologne • Melbourne • Delhi
Hong Kong • Shenzhen • Singapore

Fly high.

Wild hair day.

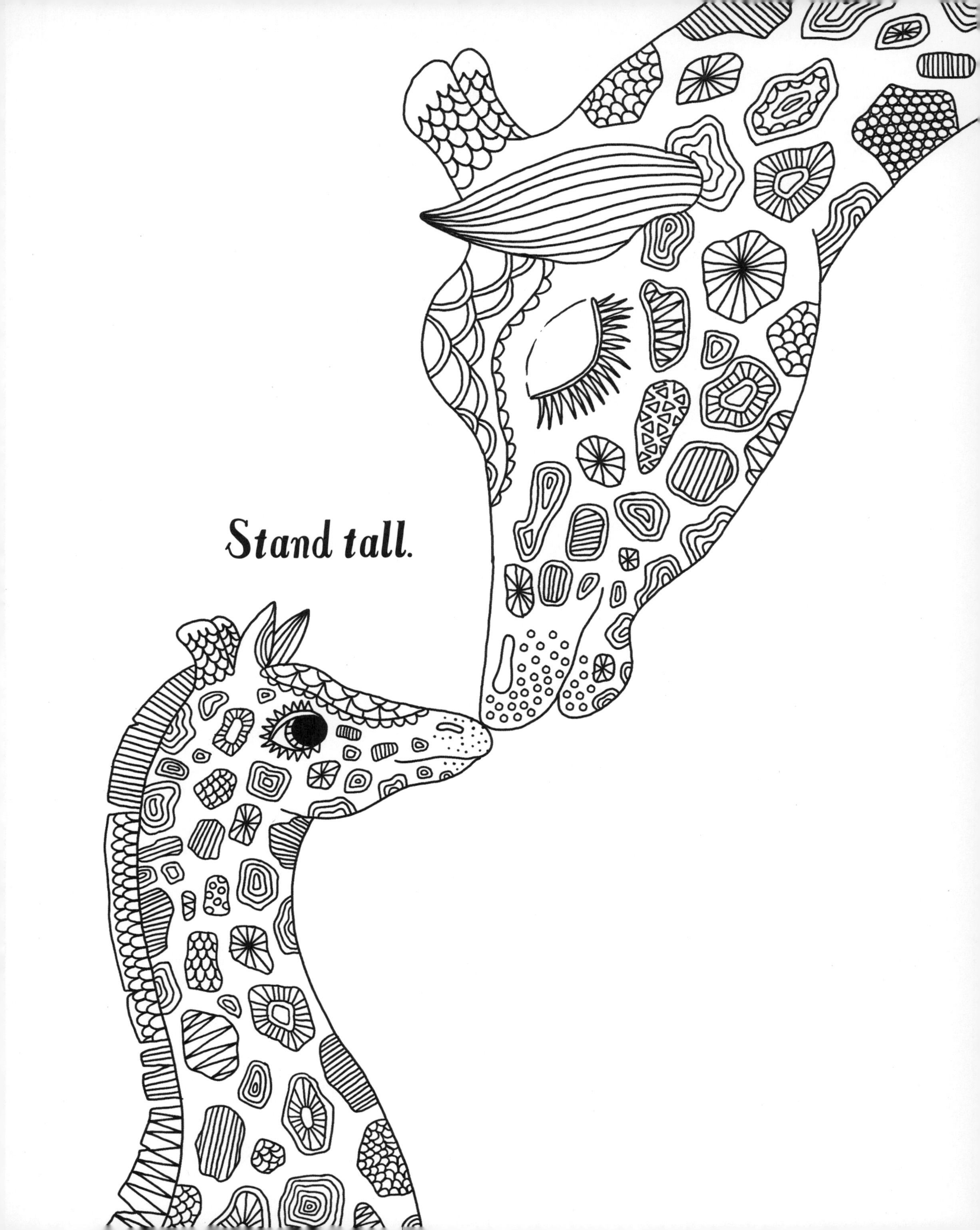
Stand tall.

Strong is beautiful.

Do something wonderful today.

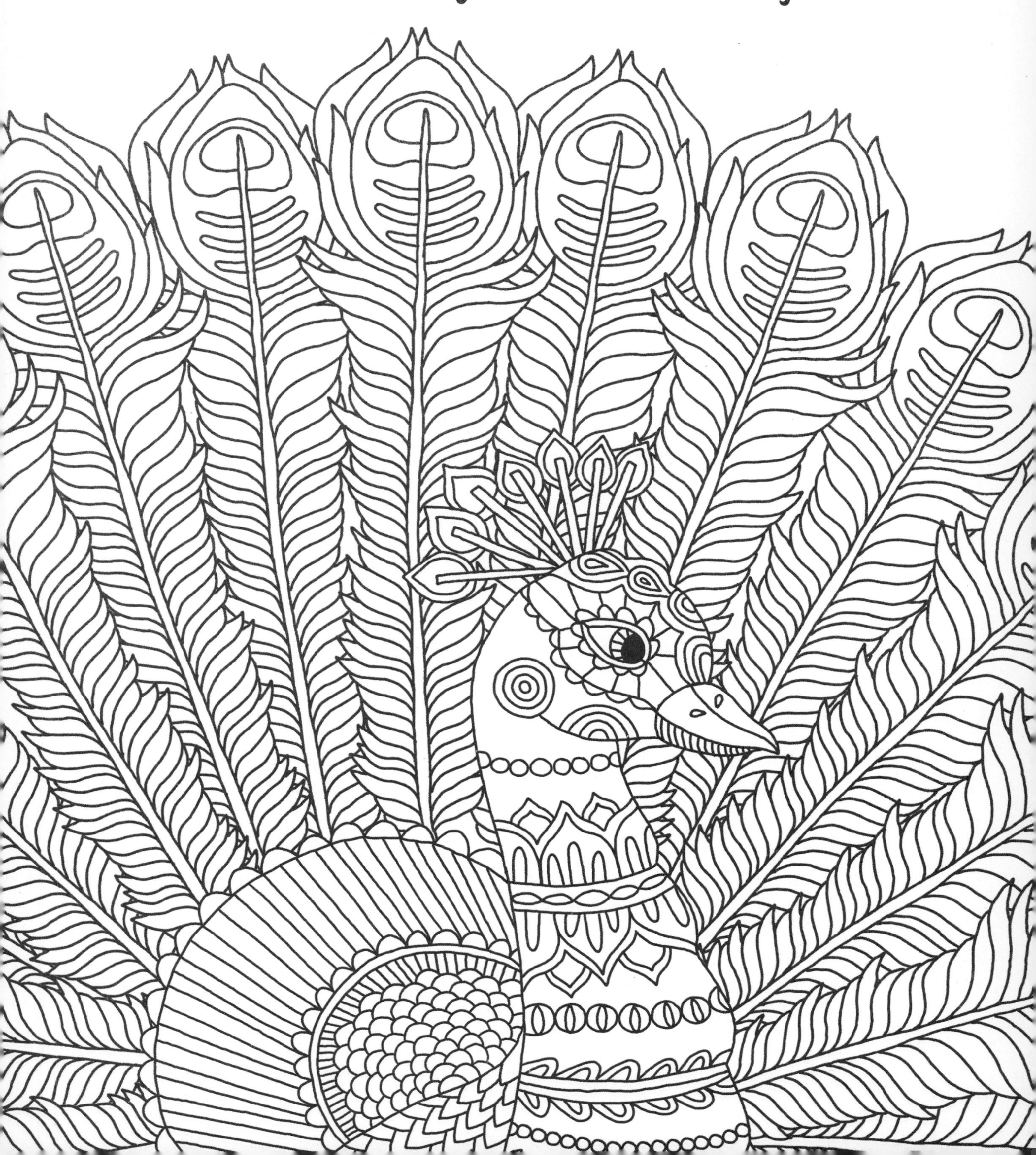

Stop and take it all in.

Love like a penguin.

Be yourself.

Travel far.

Chill out.

Be wild.

Take time to explore.

Spread your wings.

Be the colourful version of you.

Find your inner butterfly.

Colour and discover.

Practise patience.

Look closely.

Jump for joy!

Eat your greens.

Climb mountains.

Life is all about finding the right balance.

Leave your
mark.

Bear hug!

Wild dreamer.

Keep calm
and climb
a tree.

Find peace.

Stay curious.